Key Stage 2

Fiction

Carol Matchett

Name _____

Schofield & Sims

Introduction

Everyone loves reading a good story. There is nothing better than losing yourself in an adventure, discovering an amazing fictional world, or sharing the experiences of your favourite character.

This book will help you to develop your understanding of stories and to appreciate the range of fiction available. The book includes many extracts from well-known stories, which will help you to understand key features of fiction writing and how they work. It also gives you ideas for developing and improving your own stories so that others will love reading them.

Finding your way around this book

Before you start using this book, write your name in the name box on the first page.

Then decide how to begin. If you want a complete course on fiction, you should work right through the book from beginning to end. Another way to use the book is to dip into it when you want to find out about a particular topic, such as fables. The Contents page will help you to find the pages you need.

Whichever way you choose, don't try to do too much at once – it's better to work through the book in short bursts.

When you have found the topic you want to study, look out for these icons, which mark different parts of the text.

This icon shows you the activities that you should complete. You write your answers in the spaces provided. You may find it useful to have a dictionary near you so that you can check any spellings you are not sure about.

This book does not include answers to the activities because there are so many different possible answers and it wouldn't be practical to list all of them. Check your answers with an adult and when you are sure that you understand the topic, put a tick in the box beside it on the Contents page. On page 40 you will find suggestions for some projects (**Now you try**), which will give you even more opportunities to improve your understanding of fiction.

Explanation

This text explains the topic and gives examples. Make sure you read it before you start the activities.

This text gives you useful background information about the subject.

Contents

Character clues 1

Activities

Scrooge is the **main character** in the story *A Christmas Carol* by Charles Dickens. You are going to read some extracts from the beginning of the story that show how the character is introduced.

1 This is the author's **description** of Scrooge. Read it and think about what it tells us about him.

> The cold within him froze his old features, nipped his pointed nose, shrivelled his cheek, stiffened his gait, made his eyes red, his thin lips blue, and spoke out in his grating voice. A frosty rime was on his head, and on his eyebrows, and his wiry chin. He carried his own low temperature always about with him …
>
> Adapted from **A Christmas Carol**
> by **Charles Dickens** (1812–1870)

gait	way of walking
rime	frost, ice

2 Read the description again. Underline the information about what he **looks like** in one colour and the information about what **sort of person** he is in another colour.

3 The author starts with the words 'The cold within him'. What does this mean? What does it tell us about Scrooge?

_____

4 What are your **impressions** of Scrooge? Do you **like** or **dislike** him? Circle your answer below and give reasons referring to the text.

I like/dislike Scrooge because _____

_____

_____ .

5 Draw a picture of what you think Scrooge looks like, on a separate piece of paper.

Character clues 2

We can **infer**, or work out, characters' **thoughts** and **motives** (reasons) from what they say or how they behave.

Activities

1 Here is an example of how Scrooge behaves. What do his **actions** tell us about him?

> The door of Scrooge's counting-house was open so that he might keep an eye upon his clerk, who in a dismal little cell beyond was copying letters. Scrooge had a very small fire, but the clerk's fire was so very much smaller that it looked like one coal. But he couldn't replenish it, for Scrooge kept the coal-box in his own room …
>
> Adapted from **A Christmas Carol**
> by **Charles Dickens** (1812–1870)

clerk	someone who keeps records or accounts
replenish	refill

2 **a** Why does Scrooge keep the coal box in his own room?

_____

b Why does Scrooge want to keep an eye upon his clerk?

_____

3 **a** Complete this sentence.

This behaviour shows us that Scrooge is _____.

b Explain your answer. _____

_____

4 Charles Dickens also shows how other people behave towards Scrooge.

> Nobody ever stopped him in the street to say, with gladsome looks, 'My dear Scrooge, how are you? When will you come to see me?'

What did other people think about Scrooge? _____

_____

Comparing characters

Activities

1 Here is some **dialogue** that takes place just before Christmas. Underline the **words spoken** by **Scrooge** in one colour and by **his nephew** in a different colour.

> 'A merry Christmas, uncle! God save you!' cried a cheerful voice. It was the voice of Scrooge's nephew …
>
> 'Bah!' said Scrooge, 'Humbug!'
>
> He had so heated himself with rapid walking in the fog, this nephew of Scrooge's, that he was all in a glow; his face was ruddy and handsome and his eyes sparkled.
>
> 'Christmas a humbug, uncle!' said Scrooge's nephew. 'You don't mean that, I am sure?'
>
> 'I do,' said Scrooge. 'Merry Christmas! What right have you to be merry? What reason have you to be merry? You're poor enough.'
>
> 'Come, then,' returned the nephew gaily. 'What right have you to be dismal? What reason have you to be morose? You're rich enough.'
>
> Scrooge having no better answer ready on the spur of the moment, said 'Bah!' again; and followed it up with 'Humbug.'
>
> Adapted from **A Christmas Carol**
> by **Charles Dickens** (1812–1870)

| ruddy | rosy, flushed |
| morose | gloomy, bad-tempered |

2 Scrooge and his nephew are very different characters. Note key **differences** in the table below. Reread the extracts on pages 4–5 to help you.

	Scrooge	His nephew
Appearance		
Behaviour towards others		
Character (mood)		
Thoughts about Christmas		

Creating characters

Explanation

When you are **creating characters** for your own stories, think about how authors **develop** their characters and show what sort of person a character is.

Example
Remember how Charles Dickens uses **descriptive details** to introduce Scrooge and his nephew.

The cold within him froze his old features, nipped his pointed nose … ←—— Scrooge
… his face was ruddy and handsome and his eyes sparkled. ←—— his nephew

Activities

1 Create two **contrasting characters**, one who is friendly, cheerful and likeable and one who is unpleasant. Note some words or phrases to **describe** your characters. Choose your words carefully.

	Likeable character	Unpleasant character
Eyes	sparkling, laughing, twinkle	
Expression		
Way of speaking		
Way of walking or moving		

2 When you write a story, you can develop your characters through their **actions** and **speech**. Imagine your two characters met in the street. What would they say?

Likeable character

Unpleasant character

Settings

The **setting** of a story is **where** and **when** it takes place. Settings can be familiar places, such as a school or a house, or they can be unfamiliar – set in the past or in an imaginary world.

Authors use **description** to help readers imagine the setting. The descriptive **details** help us **visualise** or picture the places.

Activities

1. Here is the opening of a story called 'The Selfish Giant' by Oscar Wilde. Read this section of the story and try to **picture the setting** that is described.

The Selfish Giant

Every afternoon, as they were coming from school, the children used to go and play in the Giant's garden.

It was a large lovely garden, with soft green grass. Here and there over the grass stood beautiful flowers like stars, and there were twelve peach trees that in the springtime broke out into delicate blossoms of pink and pearl, and in the autumn bore rich fruit. The birds sat on the trees and sang so sweetly that the children used to stop their games in order to listen to them. 'How happy we are here!' they cried to each other.

Adapted from the **The Selfish Giant**
by **Oscar Wilde** (1854–1900)

---

2. Go back and read the passage again. Underline the **details** that helped you to **picture** the garden.

3. Write down **four phrases** with **adjectives** that **describe** things in the garden.

_____

_____

4. **a** Find and copy a **simile** used to describe something in the garden.

_____

   b Why did the writer use this simile?

_____

Comparing settings

The story then describes what happens when the Giant scares the children away and builds a high wall round the garden to keep them out.

1 The garden is very **different** from the first description. Underline the **details** that show what the garden is like now.

> Then the Spring came. Only in the garden of the Selfish Giant it was still winter.
>
> The birds did not care to sing in it, and the trees forgot to blossom. Once a beautiful flower put its head out from the grass, but it was so sorry for the children that it slipped back into the ground again, and went off to sleep.
>
> The only people who were pleased were the Snow and the Frost. 'Spring has forgotten this garden,' they cried, 'so we will live here all the year round.' The Snow covered up the grass with her great white cloak, and the Frost painted all the trees silver. Then they invited the North Wind to stay with them, and he came. He roared all day about the garden and blew the chimney-pots down. Then the Hail came. Every day for three hours he rattled on the roof of the castle till he broke most of the slates, and then he ran round and round the garden as fast as he could go.
>
> Adapted from **The Selfish Giant**
> by **Oscar Wilde** (1854–1900)

2 **Compare** the two descriptions. Summarise the differences in the table below.

	Description 1 (page 8)	**Description 2** (page 9)
What grows		
Sounds		
Colours		

3 On a separate piece of paper, draw a picture to show what the Giant's garden looks like at this point in the story. Label the picture with **words** and **phrases** from the description.

Mood and atmosphere

Explanation

Setting descriptions also create **moods** and **atmosphere**. They can make you feel something about a place or what might happen there.

Example **dark**, **shadowy** setting → feels **threatening** – you expect something awful to happen

magical setting → feels **exciting** – you expect all sorts of amazing things

Activities

1. Think about the **two descriptions** of the Giant's garden. How do they make you **feel** about the garden? Write your answers in the thought bubbles below.

Description 1　　　　　　　　　　　　**Description 2**

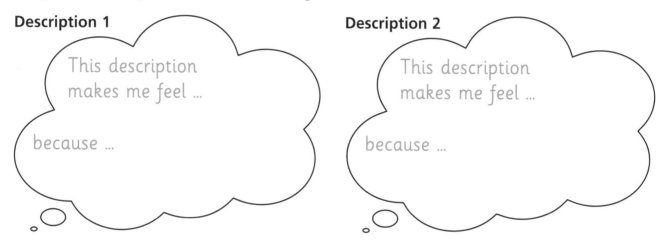

This description makes me feel …

because …

This description makes me feel …

because …

2. Reread the **second description** of the garden on page 9. Think about **how** the author has created this **mood**.

3. a What did these visitors to the garden do?

The North Wind _____

The Hail _____

b Why did the writer describe the visitors in this way? _____

_____

4. 'The trees forgot to blossom'. What does this make you **think** and **feel** about the garden?

_____

_____

You can read the story 'The Selfish Giant' in *The Happy Prince and Other Stories* by Oscar Wilde.

Fiction

Describing settings

When you are **creating a setting** for a story, think about how authors use description to **develop** their settings. Use **details** to help your reader picture the place where the events take place. Choose words carefully. Remember, the right words can create clear pictures and suggest **moods** and **feelings**.

Activities

1 You are writing a story set in a **real place** such as a busy playground, a shopping centre or a high street. Picture your setting. Fill in **details** to complete the **description** below. Choose words and phrases to make the setting come alive.

It was _____. There were _____

_____. Here and there _____

_____.

All around _____. Close by _____

_____.

2 Now picture an **imaginary place** such as a wizard's workshop, or another planet. Fill in details about the new setting to complete the description. Choose words and phrases to make the reader feel amazed.

It was _____. There were _____

_____. Here and there _____

_____.

All around _____. Close by _____

_____.

3 Read through your descriptions. Think about the pictures and effects you were trying to create. See if you can **improve** any of your word choices.

Did you know?

One early story in English, set in an imaginary world, was *Gulliver's Travels* by Jonathan Swift (published in 1726). Gulliver, the hero, visits many strange worlds: Lilliput, where all the people are tiny; Brobdingnag, where the people are as tall as steeples; and the flying island of Laputa.

Story openings 1

Explanation

The start of a story is important. It creates a **first impression**. When you read the opening of a story, look for clues about the characters, setting and what the story is about.

Activities

1 Here is an extract from the start of a story. See if you can work out **who is telling** the story and **what it is about**. Underline the **clues** that tell you.

> **Monday**
>
> Okay, okay. So hang me. I killed the bird. For pity's sake, I'm a cat. It's practically my *job* to go creeping round the garden after sweet little eensy-weensy birdy-pies that can hardly fly from one hedge to another. So what am I supposed to do when one of the poor feathery little flutterballs just throws itself into my mouth? I mean, it practically landed on my paws. It could have *hurt* me.
>
> Okay, okay. So I biffed it. Is that any reason for Ellie to cry in my fur so hard I almost drown and squeeze me so hard I almost choke?
>
> 'Ow Tuffy!' she says, all sniffles and red eyes and piles of wet tissues. 'Ow Tuffy. How could you do that?'
>
> How could I do that? I'm a cat. How did I know there was going to be such a giant great fuss …
>
> From **The Diary of a Killer Cat**
> by *Anne Fine*

2 Who is telling this story? _____ .

How do you know? _____

_____

3 Write a one-sentence **summary** of what has happened.

_____

4 From what you have read, what do you think the story will be about?

_____

Exploring points of view

Explanation

Stories can be told from different **points of view**. A 'point of view' means who is telling the story or through whose eyes we see the events. Some stories are in the **first person**, as if one of the characters is telling the story. Some stories are in the **third person**, as if someone else is telling us what happened, but they might still follow the events through the eyes of one particular character.

It is important to recognise through whose eyes we see events, because the events may seem different from another point of view.

Activities

1   What do we learn about the **character** of Tuffy from the extract on page 12?

_____

_____

2   What do we learn about the **character** of Ellie from the same extract?

_____

_____

3   Ellie's version of the events might be very different from Tuffy's. Write Ellie's diary for the same day. Use **evidence** about Ellie's thoughts and feelings from the extract on page 12.

> Monday

Did you know?

Many of the very early novels were written as diaries, journals or first-person accounts. *Robinson Crusoe*, a novel by Daniel Defoe (published in 1719), is an imaginary first-person account of a man shipwrecked on a desert island.

Story openings 2

Explanation

Sometimes a story opens with a **dialogue** or conversation between characters. The dialogue introduces the **characters** and **events**, giving clues to what the story is about.

Activities

1 Here is a section of **dialogue** from the opening of a story. Look for clues about the characters, their situation and what the story is about.

> 'It's so dreadful to be poor!' sighed Meg, looking down at her old dress.
>
> 'I don't think it's fair for some girls to have plenty of pretty things, and other girls nothing at all,' added little Amy, with an injured sniff.
>
> 'We've got Father and Mother and each other,' said Beth, contentedly, from her corner.
>
> The four young faces on which the firelight shone brightened at the cheerful words, but darkened again as Jo said sadly:
>
> 'We haven't got Father, and shall not have him for a long time.' She didn't say 'perhaps never' but each silently added it, thinking of Father far away, where the fighting was.
>
> From **Little Women**
> by **Louisa May Alcott** (1832–1888)

2 **a** What do we learn about the **four characters** from this dialogue?

_____

_____

_____

_____ .

  b What do we learn about the **problems** they have as the story begins?

_____

_____ .

3 Write a **question** you have about the characters or the events they talk about.

_____

Dialogue

Dialogue is important in stories because it helps to **develop characters** and show their feelings. How the words are spoken is just as important as what is said.

Example muttered   whispered anxiously   said with a sigh

Phrases like these help to **suggest** the thoughts and feelings of characters.

Activities

1 Reread the **dialogue** on page 14. Use a different colour to underline the words spoken by each of the **four characters**. Circle the words and phrases that show how their words are spoken.

  a What can you tell about the **mood** and **feelings** of the characters?

  _____

  _____

  _____

  b Which of the characters seems the most **cheerful**? How can you tell?

  _____ , because _____ .

2 What do you think the characters are thinking after Jo has spoken? Write your answer in the thought bubble.

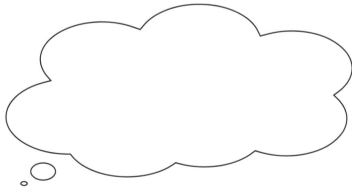

3 What might the story be about, based on what you have read?

  _____

Little Women was first published in America in 1868. It was so popular that the writer, Louisa May Alcott, immediately wrote a sequel featuring the same characters.

Writing dialogue

Explanation

When you are writing stories, use **dialogue** to help **develop characters** and show their moods and feelings. Use dialogue between characters to **explain events** or move along the action.

Activities

1 Remember that how words are spoken helps show a character's feelings. Sort these phrases into the right box, according to the **feelings** they show.

beamed Amina	he grumbled	he said with a smile
replied with a sniff	she said with a frown	grinned Leo
he added pleasantly	in a cheerful voice	scowled Greg
he said, laughing	with a heavy sigh	muttered Dad grimly

Happy and cheerful	Unhappy or discontented

2 a You are writing a story about a modern-day family with a problem. Write an **opening dialogue** to introduce the **characters** and their **problem**. Use phrases like those in activity 1 to show the feelings of your characters.

_____

_____

_____

_____

_____

b Read your dialogue aloud to see if it sounds effective. Does it show your characters and explain their problem?

Fiction

Writing a play script

Explanation

Stories are sometimes filmed or turned into **plays**. Plays, films or television programmes all need a **script** for the actors to follow. A script tells the actors what lines to say and gives **stage directions** showing how the character might act or speak.

Activities

1 Here is an example of what a **script** might look like. Label each box with a letter from the list below to show the different parts of the script.

Scene 1: *In the garden* ☐

Enter Ellie, holding her cat Tuffy.

Ellie ☐ *(sobbing)*: ☐ Ow Tuffy! Ow Tuffy. How could you do that? ☐

Ellie blows her nose noisily on a tissue. ☐

> **A** speaker's name
> **B** line to be spoken
> **C** stage direction showing **how** to say the line
> **D** stage direction giving an action or movement
> **E** scene setting

2 **a** *Little Women* is going to be made into a play. Write a script for the **opening scene** based on the extract on page 14. Use the **layout** and **features** shown above.

Scene 1: *In the living room*

Meg, Jo, Beth and Amy are seated around the room.

Meg *(sighing)*: It's so dreadful to be poor!

_____

_____

_____

_____

_____

b Try out your script. Be the **director**. Cast your scene and let the actors act out your script.

Traditional stories 1

Explanation

Traditional stories were first told a long time ago. They feature familiar **characters** such as princes and farmers, and **traditional settings** such as woods and castles. These stories often have **common patterns** or events that remind you of other traditional stories you know.

Activities

1   Here is a traditional story. As you read it, see if you recognise any **familiar features** or patterns from other traditional stories you know.

The Magic Bottle

Long ago there lived a rich and powerful King. Because he was a king, people were always giving him wonderful gifts. One of these gifts was a small bluey-green bottle containing a magic liquid – just one drop would keep a dying man alive.

As you might guess, the King guarded the bottle carefully.

One day, the court was saddened to hear that the most gallant of all the King's knights was dying. In his youth, this man had fought bravely in many of the King's great battles. He was a hero, respected by everyone. Now he was old and dying. His only wish was to stay alive a little longer to see the birth of his first grandchild.

'Just one drop of the magic liquid would save him,' the court doctor told the King.

'Certainly not,' replied the King. 'Not even half a drop. This precious liquid is meant for someone really important.'

The doctor did not dare to argue with the King.

A short time later a young servant who worked for the King was badly injured when falling from his horse. The young man was popular at court and everyone was very disturbed by the news.

'He is so young,' pleaded the Queen. 'He is the same age as our own dear son. Just one drop of the magic liquid would save him.'

'Certainly not,' replied the King, 'This precious liquid is meant for someone really special, not a mere servant.'

Even the Queen could not argue with the King.

A few years later the King's chief adviser and closest friend became very ill. Gathering all his strength, the man went to visit the King to ask for one drop of the magic liquid from the bluey-green bottle. But the King refused even him and hid the bottle in his private chamber.

The years passed and the bluey-green bottle remained unused. Then one day the King himself was taken ill. The King's condition became worse and worse and the doctors did not know what to do. Eventually, the King ordered his servant to bring him the bluey-green bottle.

At once the King grabbed the bottle. He pulled out the cork. He put the bottle to his lips. He tipped back his head, expecting to taste the magic liquid that would save his life … but there was nothing. There was nothing in the bottle!

You see, the bottle had been left for so long that the magic liquid had all dried up! So with a terrible sigh, the King died. The magic liquid, guarded for so long, had saved no-one, not even the King. And what became of the bottle? Well, that was kept and put on display to remind people of what had happened.

Adapted from **The Magic Bottle**, a European folk tale

2   Find examples of these **traditional story features** in the story.

Feature/convention	Example in 'The Magic Bottle'
Traditional characters	The main character is a King.
Traditional settings	
Magical events or objects	
Familiar events and patterns	

Traditional stories 3

Traditional stories often have a familiar **theme** or message, which is shown through the characters, their choices and what happens to them. Usually good characters are rewarded and bad ones are punished.

Activities

1 **a** Do you think the King is a '**good**' character or a '**bad**' character?

good ☐   bad ☐

b Give **reasons** for your choice.

_____

_____

_____ .

2 Underline **three** words that you think best **describe** the character of the King.

| caring | mean | selfish | generous | wise | foolish | kind | loyal |

3 What is the **theme** or message of the story 'The Magic Bottle'?

_____

_____

4 The King makes bad choices in the story. How could the story have ended happily?

_____

_____

_____

Traditional tales were originally told or sung to music rather than written down. Centuries ago, people would gather round to hear the tales of the storyteller. The same stories were retold for hundreds of years before anyone wrote them down.

Plotting the main events

Traditional stories usually have simple **plots**, which make them ideal for storytelling. You can use a **flow chart** or storyboard to plot the **main events** in a story. Then use it to help you tell the story in your own words.

Activities

1 Here is a **flow chart** for you to plot the **main events** in the story 'The Magic Bottle'. Complete the flow chart. Then use it to practise **retelling** the story in your own words.

> The King had a bottle of magic liquid that could keep people alive.

↓

> One day, one of the King's knights was dying.

↓

> The King would not give him any of the magic liquid.

↓

> A short time later,

↓

>

↓

>

↓

>

↓

>

↓

>

Fables 1

Explanation

A **fable** is a type of **traditional story**. It tends to be short and often ends with a **moral** that tells us what we should learn from the story. The **characters** in a fable are often **animals** but they behave just like humans! We learn from the mistakes they make.

Activities

1 Read this **fable** about a dog. Think about what the **moral** of the story might be.

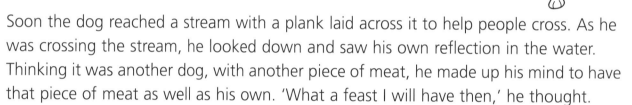

The Dog and the Bone

A dog sniffing round the back of a butcher's stall had found a juicy piece of meat. As he trotted home carrying the meat in his mouth, he looked forward to devouring it.

Soon the dog reached a stream with a plank laid across it to help people cross. As he was crossing the stream, he looked down and saw his own reflection in the water. Thinking it was another dog, with another piece of meat, he made up his mind to have that piece of meat as well as his own. 'What a feast I will have then,' he thought.

The dog made a sudden grab for the meat reflected in the water. But as soon as he opened his mouth, his own piece of meat fell out, disappearing into the water – never to be seen again. And so the dog went home hungry – but perhaps wiser.

2 Tick which of these **morals** best fits this story.

- Don't put off until tomorrow what you can do today. ☐

- Slow and steady wins the day. ☐

- Don't be greedy; be satisfied with what you have. ☐

- If at first you don't succeed, try, try, and try again. ☐

Did you know?

'The Dog and the Bone' was probably first told in the sixth century BC in Ancient Greece by a man called **Aesop** ('ee–sop'). He made up lots of fables, which have been popular ever since.

Fables 2

3 Write a one or two-sentence precis of the **fable** 'The Dog and the Bone'.

A greedy dog _____

_____ .

4 The dog was foolish and made a big mistake. What might he be thinking at the **end** of the story?

I feel …

I wish I had …

Next time …

5 Think of an idea for another **fable** featuring the character of the foolish dog.

Here is the **moral** for your story: **Look before you leap.**

In the box below, **plan** a **three-paragraph story**, like 'The Dog and the Bone'. Think about what the dog might do to show that this moral is true.

Paragraph 1: beginning
Paragraph 2: middle
Paragraph 3: end

A modern retelling 1

Activities

1   Here is a **modern version** of the traditional story 'The Old Woman and the Vinegar Bottle'. As you read, underline **details** that show this is a modern version of the story.

Carrie and her Wishes

Carrie sat down on the stripy sofa with a contented smile. It had been a hard day, but here she was at last in her new home. Yes, it was a bit of a mess at the moment. And yes, it needed a lick of paint … but it was hers.

Over the next few weeks, Carrie spent all her spare time painting and decorating. When she had finished she was delighted with the result. She proudly emailed all her friends, inviting them over to her cosy little flat.

A little while later, Carrie was asked to deliver a parcel to a lovely new house in a rather grand street. It had a gravel driveway, a double garage, a beautiful garden … and even a small swimming pool.

Carrie thought of her tiny little flat and then thought about this beautiful house. 'It's so unfair. I wish I could live in a beautiful house like this with a gravel driveway, a garden and a swimming pool.'

Now, it just so happened that the Lottery Fairy heard this wish and with a puff of smoke, a scattering of stars and a few magic words, Carrie found herself living in the beautiful new house!

Carrie was thrilled. She texted all her friends and invited them over. They had barbecues in the garden and splashed in the pool.

A modern retelling 2

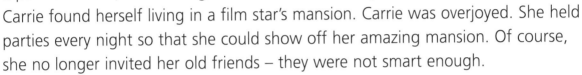

One day, Carrie was idly reading a magazine article about a famous film star. There were photographs of the star posing at her home – a Hollywood mansion that had a huge swimming pool, a gym and a helipad for her private helicopter.

Carrie looked at her own house with its little, tiny swimming pool. 'It's so unfair. I wish I could live in a mansion like a film star.'

It just so happened that the Lottery Fairy was passing by. With a puff of smoke, a scattering of stars and a few magic words, Carrie found herself living in a film star's mansion. Carrie was overjoyed. She held parties every night so that she could show off her amazing mansion. Of course, she no longer invited her old friends – they were not smart enough.

One evening at one of her parties, she overheard one guest telling another about a palace belonging to a prince. 'It has 78 rooms – all very grand – and a ballroom.'

Carrie thought of her mansion, which had just 24 rooms – and no ballroom 'It's so unfair. I wish I could live in a palace. It would be so grand and regal.'

Now, it just so happened that the Lottery Fairy was at the party. With a puff of smoke, a scattering of stars and a few magic words, Carrie found herself living in a palace.

Carrie was overjoyed for a time. She held grand balls every week and everything seemed wonderful. But on the days when there was no ball, no-one visited. The servants did not dare to speak to her. Her old friends had long since forgotten her, as she had never replied to their texts. Soon Carrie became lonely in her 78-room palace. She began to remember how happy she had once been in her little one-bedroom flat …

2   What do you think will happen now? How will the story end? Write your **predictions** before you turn the page.

_____

_____

_____

Activities

1 This is how the story ends.

> Now it just so happened that the Lottery Fairy was tired of Carrie and her wishes. Three wishes was enough for anyone. So with a great cloud of smoke, a huge thunderbolt and a few rather angry magic words, Carrie found herself sitting on her old stripy sofa back in her little one-bedroom flat.

a Does the story end as you thought? ☐ Yes ☐ No

b Explain your answer.

_____

_____

2 Do you think Carrie was happy at the end of the story? Give reasons for your answer.

_____

_____

3 **Why** do you think the writer chose to write the story in a **modern setting**?

_____

_____

_____

4 Would you still describe 'Carrie and her Wishes' as a **traditional story**? Explain your answer.

_____

_____

5 **a** In what way does the story remind you of the fable 'The Dog and the Bone'?

_____

b How are the two stories different? Give **two** ways in which they are different.

_____

_____

Comparing stories 2

Explanation

Traditional stories are enjoyed all over the world. Although stories from **different cultures** reflect their different settings, customs and beliefs, the **same themes** are found all over the world.

Example good defeats evil
courage, wisdom and kindness are rewarded

Activities

1 Read this extract from the start of a **traditional story** from China about a young girl called Yeh-Shen. It may remind you of another story you know.

> **Yeh-Shen**
>
> Many, many moons ago, there lived a powerful chief named Chief Wu. Chief Wu's wife gave birth to a healthy baby girl named Yeh-Shen and they were very happy. But when her mother died, the little girl was left to be brought up by her stepmother.
>
> Now, the stepmother did not like Yeh-Shen, for the little girl was more beautiful than her own daughter. So the stepmother treated poor Yeh-Shen very badly. She gave Yeh-Shen all the worst jobs and only the meanest morsels of food.
>
> Yeh-Shen shared the little food she had with a beautiful fish whom she visited every day. At least she had a friend to talk to – for the moment …

2 **a** What well-known story does Yeh-Shen remind you of? _____

b In what way is the story of Yeh-Shen the **same** as and **different** from the story you know?

	Same	Different
Characters		
Events		

3 Reread the **last sentence** of the extract. What does this suggest will happen?

_____

4 You have read the **start** of the story. How do you think the story will **end**? What do you think will happen to Yeh-Shen at the end? Explain your **predictions**, referring to what you have read.

_____

Story structure

Explanation

The **structure** of a story is its shape or pattern – how it builds up from the beginning to the end. Stories can be structured in different ways. 'Carrie and her Wishes' (pages 24–26) is a **circle story** because the main character starts and ends in the same place.

Activities

1 You can draw a diagram to show the **structure** of a story. Complete this **flow chart** to show the circular structure of 'Carrie and her Wishes'.

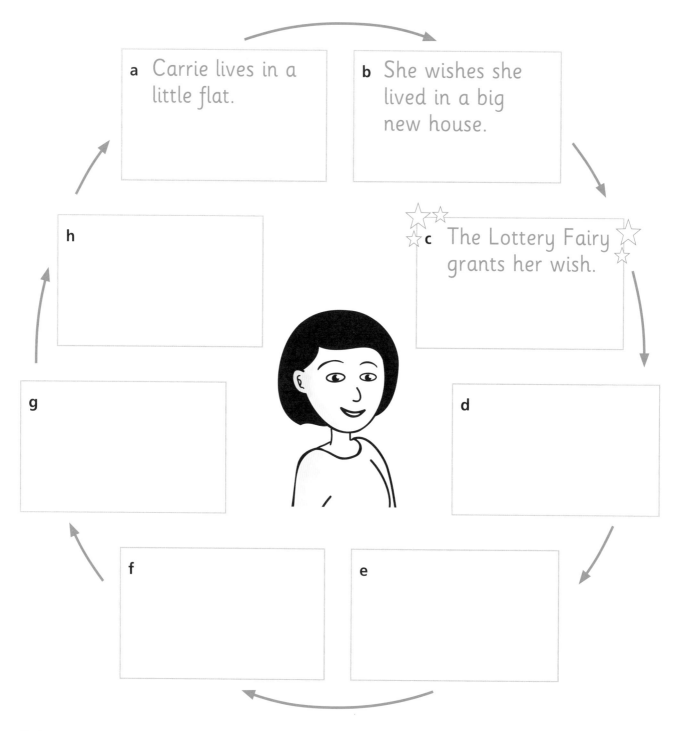

a Carrie lives in a little flat.

b She wishes she lived in a big new house.

c The Lottery Fairy grants her wish.

h

g

d

f

e

Plotting your own story

1 Use stories you read to help you plan your own stories. Make up your own **circle story** based on 'Carrie and her Wishes' (pages 24–26). Use the same idea of someone who keeps wishing for something more, but change the main character and other details. Plot the **main events** of your story, noting ideas on this flow chart to show the **circular plot**.

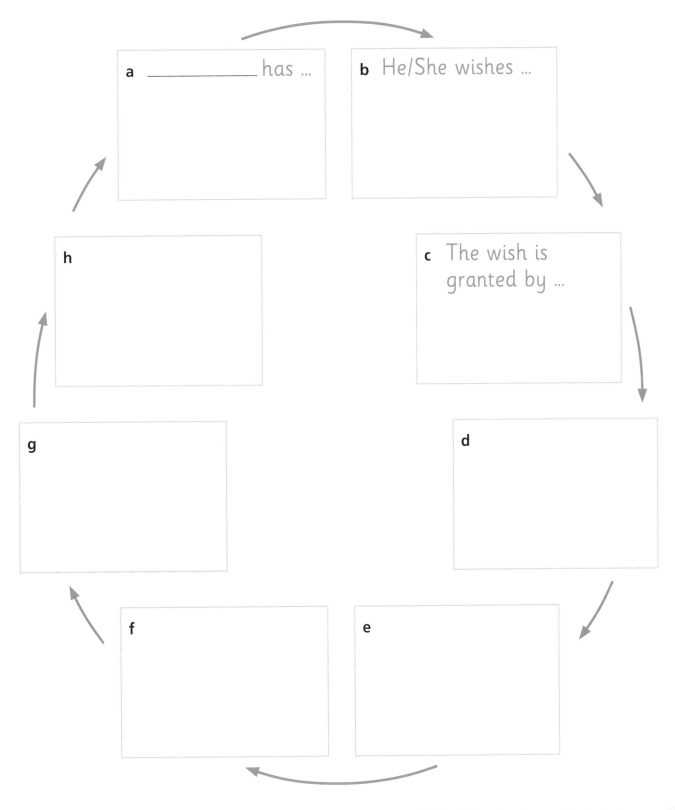

a _____ has ...

b He/She wishes ...

c The wish is granted by ...

d

e

f

g

h

Reader response 1

Explanation

As you read a story, it is important to think about your **response** to events and characters, and how you feel at different points. You might **record** your response in a reading journal or make notes in the margins around the text.

Activities

Here is an extract from a Greek legend. In this part of the story, the hero Perseus has been given the task of killing the terrible Gorgon Medusa.

1 Read the extract and think about your **response**. Underline any words or phrases that have a **strong impact**. Note your thoughts or feelings beside each paragraph.

Clouds scudded across the moon as Perseus stood at the mouth of the cave. He took a deep breath and crept into the darkness. In the dim light he could just make out greyish movements.

Crouching in the shadows he edged closer, hugging the cave wall. Muffled moans told him that the Gorgons were sleeping. Their leathery wings were folded but still their hair coiled and writhed in a swaying mass of serpents.

Silently, Perseus drew his sword. But which was Medusa? He must be certain; he would have only one chance. Just a glance into Medusa's eyes and he would be turned to stone. Could he use his shield as a mirror? Yes, there in the reflection was the sleeping Medusa.

Now, blood pounding, he seized his sword. Swinging it high above his head, he pounced. Startled, Medusa awoke – but Perseus was too quick. Leaping forward, with one swift and mighty blow he sliced off the Gorgon's head. Suddenly the cave was full of fury. The Gorgon's sisters awoke with blood-curdling screams, lashing out, spitting venom. Grabbing the Medusa's head and scooping it into a sack, Perseus fled …

scud move rapidly	**coil** wind round	**writhe** squirm
serpent snake	**blood-curdling** terrifying	**venom** poison

2 What is the **overall effect** created in the passage?

_____

_____

_____

Reader response 2

Explanation

When you reread a passage, you can look at how a response was brought about. Look carefully at how the story is written and at the **choice of words**. Think about why words were chosen and the likely **effect** or impact of the words, phrases and sentences on the reader.

Activities

1 Reread each paragraph of the story on page 30 and think about how different **effects** were created. Explain your ideas, referring to the text.

Paragraph 1: the mood and the words and phrases that create it

Paragraph 2: how the Gorgons are introduced and the effect this has

Paragraph 3: why the writer uses questions

Paragraph 4: how the atmosphere changes and how this effect has been achieved

2 Write three or four sentences **summarising** the story.

Tension and suspense 1

Explanation

Suspense is an important part of a story – it keeps us reading. Things often start quietly and then the suspense **builds up** through a series of events, leaving you expecting something to happen at any moment but unsure what it will be.

Activities

Here is an extract from *The Wind in the Willows* by Kenneth Grahame. In this part of the story, Mole has entered the Wild Wood against the advice of his friend the Rat.

1 As you read the extract, feel the **build-up of tension**.

The Wild Wood

There was nothing to alarm him at first entry. Twigs crackled under his feet, logs tripped him, funguses on stumps resembled caricatures, and startled him for a moment; but that was all fun and exciting. It led him on to where the light was less, and trees crouched nearer and nearer, and holes made ugly mouths at him on either side.

Everything was very still now. The dusk advanced on him steadily, rapidly, gathering in behind and before; and the light seemed to be draining away like floodwater.

Then the faces began.   FEAR FACTOR ☐

It was over his shoulder, and indistinctly, that he first thought he saw a face: a little evil wedge-shaped face, looking out at him from a hole. When he turned and confronted it, the thing had vanished.

He quickened his pace, telling himself cheerfully not to begin imagining things, or there would be simply no end to it. He passed another hole, and another, and another; and then – yes! – no! – yes! Certainly a little narrow face, with hard eyes, had flashed up for an instant from a hole, and was gone. Then suddenly every hole, far and near, seemed to possess its face, all fixing on him glances of malice and hatred: all hard-eyed and evil and sharp.

If he could only get away from the holes in the banks, he thought, there would be no more faces. He swung off the path and plunged into the untrodden places of the wood.

Then the whistling began.   FEAR FACTOR ☐

Very faint and shrill it was, and far behind him, when he first heard it; but somehow it made him hurry forward. Then, still very faint and shrill, it sounded far ahead of him, and made him hesitate and want to go back. As he halted in indecision it broke out on either side, and seemed to be passed on throughout the whole length of the wood to its furthest limit. They were up and alert and ready, whoever they were! And he – he was alone, and unarmed, and far from any help; and the night was closing in.

Then the pattering began.

FEAR FACTOR ☐

He thought it was only falling leaves at first, so slight and delicate was the sound of it. Then as it grew it took on a regular rhythm, and he knew it for nothing else but the pat-pat-pat of little feet, still a very long way off. Was it in front or behind? It seemed to be first one, then the other, then both. It grew and it multiplied, till from every quarter it seemed to be closing in on him.

The pattering increased till it sounded like sudden hail on the dry-leaf carpet spread around him. The whole wood seemed to be running now, running hard, hunting, chasing, closing in round something or – somebody?

In panic, he began to run too, aimlessly, he knew not whither. He ran up against things, he fell over things and into things, and he darted under things and dodged round things. At last he took refuge in the dark deep hollow of an old beech tree, which offered shelter, concealment – perhaps even safety, but who could tell?

FEAR FACTOR ☐

And as he lay there panting and trembling, and listened to the whistlings and the patterings outside, he knew it at last, in all its fullness, that dread thing which other little dwellers in field and hedgerow had encountered here, and known as their darkest moment – that thing which the Rat had vainly tried to shield him from – the Terror of the Wild Wood!

Adapted from **The Wind in the Willows** by **Kenneth Grahame** (1859–1932)

caricature	funny picture of a person
malice	ill will, desire to do harm
whither	where to
refuge	place of safety

2   Try reading the extract **aloud**. Use your voice to convey the changes in **mood** effectively.

Language for effect

Explanation

Writers **build suspense** through the way they tell the story and how they describe events. The choice of words and details, the **description** of sounds and feelings and reactions all help to build the sense of uncertainty and unease. Different **sentence structures** draw us in, make us wonder and build up the tension.

Activities

1 Reread 'The Wild Wood' on pages 32–33. Underline words, phrases or sentences that help to **build suspense**. As you read, put a fear factor score in each of the boxes shown, using the scale below.

> **1 a little on edge** **2 rather nervous** **3 scared** **4 very frightened** **5 terrified**

2 Look for examples of these **techniques** in the passage. Write some examples in the boxes below.

Technique	Examples
Descriptive language, including imagery – similes and metaphors	holes made ugly mouths at him
Doubts, uncertainty – is something real or is it imagined?	When he turned and confronted it, the thing had vanished.
Special techniques – repeated words or phrases to draw us in	
Different sentence types – questions that make us wonder, exclamations to surprise	

Creating suspense

Explanation

When writing your own stories, remember to **build up** the excitement and **suspense** at the most important point in your story. Think about how other authors do this and use the same methods in your story. Start quietly and build up to the most exciting moment. Use **descriptive details**, **sentence structures** and **techniques** that draw the reader in.

Activities

1 Imagine that a character in your story is in a dark place. It is late at night. Something terrible is going to happen – but what … and when? Note ideas, words and phrases you might use to **build suspense**. Choose words carefully; think about the **effect**.

Description of sounds (some quiet and worrying; some loud and frightening)	**Worrying details** (glimpses: vague and unclear – leave some doubt)

Building suspense

Character's reaction (showing what the character is thinking)	**Questions, exclamations or repeated phrases** to draw the reader in

2 Use your ideas to write this part of the story on a separate piece of paper. Say and **improve** each sentence before you write it, thinking about the effect you are making.

Genre conventions 1

Explanation

There are many different types, or **genres**, of story. Adventure, mystery, fantasy and science fiction are examples of genres. Each genre has special features and **conventions** that you might recognise – familiar plots, characters, settings, situations and events and themes.

Example ghost story ➔ set in a spooky place

tension, surprises, something to frighten the main characters

Activities

1 Here are some **story genres**.

adventure	mystery	science fiction

fantasy world	realism	ghost story

Read the **blurb** on the back of these books and decide which **genre** each book belongs to. Write the genre on the label. Underline the **clues** in the blurb that told you what the genre was.

A series of robberies …
a strange light on the
beach … What is happening
at Sunnyways Hotel?
Who is responsible for
the thefts?

Zoë and Mick set out to
investigate in:

**The Case of the Missing
Diamonds**

'It was Meena's fault.'
'Meena did it, not me.'
That was all Meena ever
heard these days. Ever since
Malik had come to live
with them everything was
Meena's fault. And Dad
always believed Malik, not
her. That was the worst
thing of all.

On a mission to the planet Alpha III the spaceship *Crusader* comes under attack from an alien vessel. Can the crew escape through a black hole? Or will they be captured by an alien life force?

With a treasure map found in an old book, Jason Brown sets off on an action-packed search for lost treasure. The map will take him across four continents and bring him face to face with the evil Professor Claw and many other villains …

A sinister house …
A scream in the night …
No wonder Kelly is having nightmares. But are they nightmares … or are those events real?

Kuldip steps through a doorway and finds himself in the strange world of Talavon. The forest people of Talavon live in fear of the evil Emperor. Can Kuldip help them? And can he find his way back to the real world?

Did you know?

Science fiction (or sci-fi) stories first appeared at the end of the nineteenth century. H.G. Wells was an early sci-fi writer. He wrote stories about invasions from outer space (*The War of the Worlds*) and time travel (*The Time Machine*) – themes used many times since.

Book recommendations

Explanation

Everyone has their own **favourite stories**. It is a good idea to share **recommendations** with your friends. Not everyone likes the same type of story, so always give some information about the **genre** and what the story is about so your friends know what to expect.

Activities

1 My favourite five books (and authors) are:

- _____
- _____
- _____
- _____
- _____

2 **a** My favourite story genre is _____.

b Recommend three books for people who like this genre.

Readers who like _____ (name of genre)

will enjoy these books: • _____

• _____

• _____

3 Complete this book recommendation for one of your favourite books.

I would like to recommend the book _____

_____ by _____.

I recommend this book because _____

_____.

It is about _____

_____.

I think this book will appeal to _____

because _____

_____.

Writing in different genres

Explanation

When you are writing your own stories, it is a good idea to use stories you have read as **models**. When you are **planning**, think about stories in the same **genre** – this will give you ideas for characters, settings, events, plots and story structures.

Activities

1 Your task is to write an entertaining or exciting story for someone **your own age**.

a Choose a **genre** you think will appeal to them: _____

b Think about other stories you have read in that genre. Note some ideas for your story.

Characters	Setting	What the story is about

c Plan your story. Use a familiar story **structure**. Keep the **plot** simple – nothing too complicated.

Beginning

Middle (build-up) – plan in paragraphs

End

d Use your plan to write your story on a separate piece of paper. As you write, think about the **style** and sound of your story. Remember it is how you tell the story that will make it **effective**, so keep rereading to check how your story sounds.

2 Let a friend read your story. Use their feedback to help you **improve** your writing.

Reading challenge

We all have our favourite sort of books – perhaps you love ghost stories or adventures. Next time you are choosing a book at school or at the library, why not set yourself the challenge of reading a book from a different genre – something you wouldn't usually choose.

Pass it on

When you finish reading a good story, pass the book on to a friend who might enjoy it. Write an intriguing message about the book and slip it inside (for example, 'The main character in this story reminds me of you!' or 'Wait until you get to chapter 6!') – but don't give away too much and spoil the plot.

Book club

Start a book club for your friends or family. Get everyone in your book club to read the same book and then you can all discuss it at your meeting. Or you could ask all the members of the book club to bring along their favourite book to recommend to the rest of the group.

Drama time

A rainy day is the ideal time to act out a story. Don't choose a story that is too complicated – a traditional story that everyone knows is ideal.

Storytelling

One of the best ways of learning to write really good stories is to start by telling good stories. Try entertaining a younger brother or sister with your storytelling. See if you can keep them interested by using different ways of building up the story and making it exciting.

Chain stories

This is a fun way of writing stories. Write the opening of a story. Leave it at an interesting point and then e-mail it or pass the story on to a friend or another member of the family. Ask them to write the next part of the story and then pass it back to you. You keep passing the story on until someone thinks of a good ending!